Teddy Bears

123

1

One teddy bear is cycling.
The wheels turn round and round;
Up the hill, then down again,
He races all around.

2

Two teddy bears are in the park,
There's lots to see and do,
They swing and slide all morning
Then play ball all afternoon.

Three teddy bears are by the sea,
The sun is warm and bright;
When they have had their picnic lunch
They like to fly their kite.

Four teddy bears are gardening,
They help to clear the weeds;
There is a lot of work to do
Before they plant their seeds.

4

Five teddy bears are skipping,
The rope turns round and round;
They count each jump they make,
As they skip along the ground.

Six teddies like to rollerskate
Together in the sun;
Up and down the path they go
Having lots of fun.

6

Seven teddy bears are climbing
High up in a tree;
They reach the top, then look around,
There is so much to see.

7

Eight teddy bears are cleaning,
There is a lot to do;
They dust and clean and polish,
Working the whole day through.

Nine teddy bears play in the snow;
They like to skate and slide
Together down a snowy slope;
They all enjoy their ride.

Ten teddy bears are warm in bed
The moon is shining bright.
They like to hear a story
In the middle of the night.

10